OPEN HIGHWAYS

a diagnostic and developmental reading program

ROLLING ALONG

Helen M. Robinson
Marion Monroe
A. Sterl Artley
Charlotte S. Huck
William A. Jenkins
Ira E. Aaron
Linguistics Advisor, Andrew Schiller

Scott, Foresman and Company

CONTENTS

Bookish

by Aileen Fisher

This little bug
has a very wise look,
crawling over
the words on my book.

Of course, he can't read,
but possibly
he's looking at things
that I can't see.

"Bookish" from *Up the Windy Hill* by Aileen Fisher. Reprinted by permission of the author.

A Joke

Adapted by arrangement with the Register and Tribune Syndicate.

The Little Old Woman and How She Kept Her Geese Warm

7

"How She Kept Her Geese Warm" from *The Little Old Woman Who Used Her Head* by Hope Newall. Reprinted by permission of Thomas Nelson & Sons, publisher.

The Little Old Woman was out in the barn.

She was getting her geese ready for bed.

She gave them some corn.

She took off their little red coats.

My geese must get very cold at night.
I have my fire and my feather bed
to keep me warm.
But my geese do not have a thing
to keep them warm.

All the geese hopped up on the roost.

The Little Old Woman shut the barn door.

She went into the house.

She went to bed.

I can not sleep.
I keep thinking about how cold
my geese must be.
I will bring them into my warm house.

The Little Old Woman
got out of bed.
She put on her coat.
She went out to the
barn to get her geese.

11

The Little Old Woman

took two geese into the house.

She took two more geese into the house.

She took the last two geese

into the house.

The Little Old Woman gave the geese

some corn.

She took off their little red coats.

The Little Old Woman went to bed.

The Little Old Woman could not sleep.

So the Little Old Woman got up.
She put a wet towel on her head.
Then she sat down to think.
She put her finger
on her nose.
She shut her eyes.
She used her head
and used her head.

14

The Little Old Woman took her bed
to the barn.

She took the roost to the house.

16

The Little Old Woman went to sleep.

How to Make a Sock Puppet

You will need a white sock.

You will need an orange crayon.

You will need a black crayon.

First lay the sock flat.

Make a big black eye.

Then draw the bill.

Color the bill orange.

Next turn the sock over.

Make a big black eye.

Draw the bill.

Color the bill orange.

Last, put your puppet on your hand.

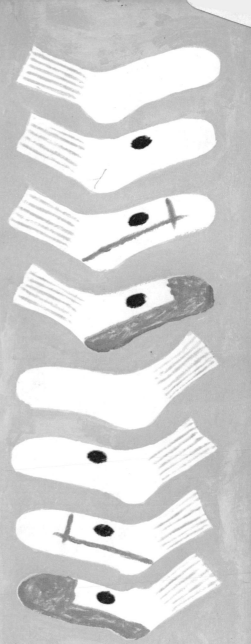

The Old Woman and the Pig

There was an old woman,   and she

bought a little pig. Oink, oink, oink.

There was an old woman, and she

bought a little pig. She didn't pay

much, 'cause he wasn't very big.

Oink, oink, oink.

I Had a Little Pig

I had a little pig, I fed him in a trough,

But he got so fat that his tail dropped off.

So I got me a hammer and I got me a nail,

And I made my little pig a brand new tail.

22

"I Had a Little Pig" from *Fun in American Folk Rhymes* by Ray Wood. Copyright, 1952, by Ray Wood. Published by J. B. Lippincott Company.

Coats   for   Katie

and

Carmen

Katie and Carmen were friends.

One day Katie was playing
at Carmen's house.
Carmen's mother asked the girls
to go to the store.
She needed some milk.

The girls went out of the house.

Carmen said, "It looks like rain.
Let's hurry, Katie."

At the store Carmen got the milk.

Katie said, "It's raining, Carmen.
We're going to get wet!"

Mr. Nelson said, "You won't
get wet, girls.
I can make raincoats for you.
I make good raincoats."

Mr. Nelson cut two big boxes.

Then he put the boxes on the girls.

"There you are," he said.

"See what good raincoats I make?

Now go on home, but be careful."

"We will," said Carmen. "Thank you."

Katie said, "We look pretty funny

in these raincoats.

But I bet we won't get wet."

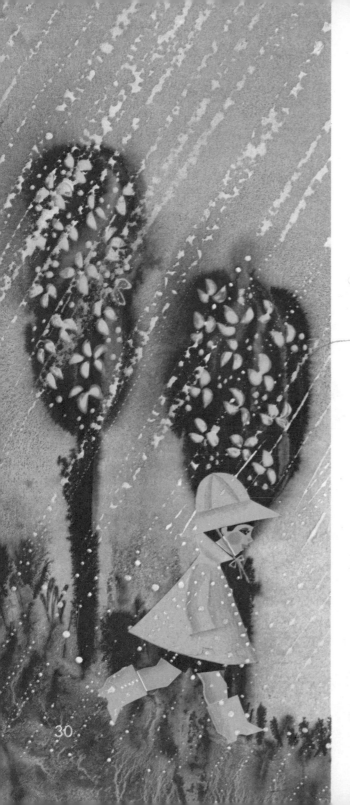

Storm

by Aileen Fisher

I have
often
wondered
why

So many
faucets
in the
sky

Could
open up
and not
run dry.

Rain

by Robert Louis Stevenson

The rain is raining all around,
It falls on field and tree,
It rains on the umbrellas here,
And on the ships at sea.

31

An Umbrella Joke

A New Place

for

Old Comic Books

Ross and Cindy saved comic books.

They never threw one away.

So there were comic books everywhere.

One day their mom got mad.

34

She said, "You've got to get rid of
these comic books.
I just won't have them all over the place.
Get them out of here, NOW!"

Ross and Cindy didn't say a word.
They picked up the comic books as fast
as they could.

Mom opened the door, and the children went out.

"Let's go find Mr. Carter," said Ross. "Maybe he can help us."

Mr. Carter was the man who took care of the building.
When he saw the children, he asked, "What do you have there?"

"Our comic books," said Cindy. "Mom won't let us keep them in the apartment."

"Bring them in here," said Mr. Carter. "We'll pick out some of the comic books to keep.
I know something we can do with them."

First, Mr. Carter put some bricks down.

Next he put a board on the bricks.

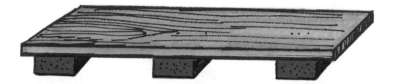

Then he put some more bricks
on top of the board.

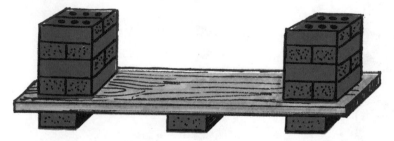

Last, Mr. Carter put another board
on top of the bricks.

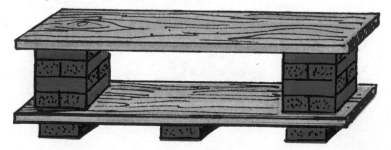

"I see what you did!" Ross said.
"You made a place for us to keep
our comic books.
Now we have a library."

"We'll tell the other children,"
said Cindy.
"They can keep their comic books
here."

Mr. Carter said, "Not just
comic books.   Other books, too."

All the children in the building
liked to come to Mr. Carter's library.
They came to read and trade
all kinds of books.

The library was a busy place.

The Gingerbread Boy

A little old woman and a little old man
lived in a little old house.

One day the little old woman made
a gingerbread boy.
She put him on the table.

The gingerbread boy jumped down and
ran out of the house.
The little old woman ran after him.

The little old man was working
in the garden.
He saw the gingerbread boy running away.
The little old man ran after him.

The gingerbread boy could run very fast.

He called to the little old man,

"I ran away from the little old woman.

And I can run away from you,

I can, I can."

The gingerbread boy came to a
cow and a pig.
The cow and the pig saw
the gingerbread boy running away.
They ran after him.

The gingerbread boy called back,

"I ran away from the little old woman.

I ran away from the little old man.

And I can run away from you,

I can, I can."

The gingerbread boy came
to some men cutting wheat.
The men saw the gingerbread boy
running away. They ran after him.

The gingerbread boy called back,

"I ran away from the little old woman.

I ran away from the little old man.

I ran away from the cow and the pig.

And I can run away from you,

I can, I can."

The gingerbread boy came to a fox.

The fox ran after the gingerbread boy.

The gingerbread boy ran very fast.

But the fox ran fast, too.

The gingerbread boy called to the fox,

"I ran away from the little old woman.

I ran away from the little old man.

I ran away from the cow and the pig.

I ran away from the men cutting wheat.

And I can run away from you,

I can, I c. . . ."

What do you think happened?

The gingerbread boy ran home.

The fox ran away.

The fox ate the gingerbread boy.

Mystery at the
Old Shack

Stan and Bud and Roger had a shack.
It was made out of old boxes.
The boys went there to play every day.

Then one day something happened.
Bud got to the shack first.
Soon Stan and Roger came along.

"Stop!" said Bud.
"Don't go in the shack.
There's something in there."

"There **is** something in the shack,"
said Roger.
"I hear it.
What do you think it is?"

"I don't know," said Stan.
"I'm scared.   Let's go home."

"I'm not scared," said Roger.

"This is a mystery.

I like a good mystery.

I'll find out what's in the shack."

So Roger went inside.

Then Roger came running out
of the shack.

"What's in there?" asked Stan.

"A cat," said Roger.
"And is she mad!"

"What's the cat so mad about?"
asked Bud.   "It's OUR shack."

The boys looked in the door
of the shack.

"I see why she's mad,"
said Bud.
"She has four kittens, and she's
afraid we'll hurt them."

"Let's go away for now," said Stan.
"We'll come back and see the kittens
in a week or two."

A Kitten

1 week old

A kitten can not open its eyes.
Do not play with it.

2 weeks old

A kitten can open its eyes.
Do not play with it yet.

3 weeks old

A kitten can walk and run now.
Do not play with it yet.

6 weeks old

A kitten gets into everything.
You can play with it now.

A Horse
in Box Canyon

There he is! It's one of our horses. We'll have to get him out.
I'll call Walt. He'll come in his helicopter.

67

Up went the helicopter with the horse.

Rex and Ernie climbed out of the canyon.

More About Helicopters

There is a policeman in this helicopter.

He is telling people about the traffic.

This helicopter is bringing people to work.

This helicopter is bringing people
to a hospital.

This helicopter is picking up astronauts.

It will take them to a ship.

How to Make a Helicopter

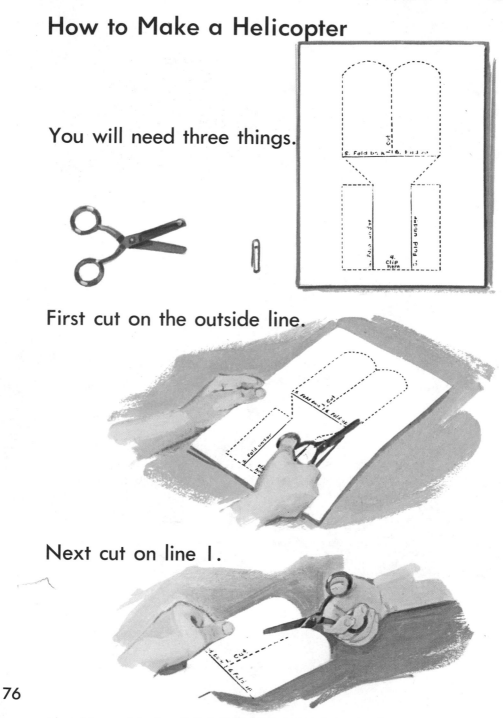

You will need three things.

First cut on the outside line.

Next cut on line 1.

Adapted by permission from *McCall's/Golden Make-It Book* designed and arranged by John Peter; illustrated by Corinne Malvern and Bob Riley. Copyright 1953 by Golden Press, Inc.

Then fold on lines 2 and 3.

Next clip together on 4.

Then fold back on line 5.

Fold up on line 6.

Last, drop your helicopter.

Debbie

Is a

Tattletale

Debbie was Vic's little sister.
Most of the time Vic thought
she was a pretty good sister.
But Debbie was a tattletale.
And this made Vic mad.

One day Debbie saw Vic eating
some cookies.
She ran to find her dad.

"Dad, Dad," said Debbie.
"Vic is eating all the cookies."
Her dad said, "Don't be a tattletale."

"But Vic is eating all the cookies,"
said Debbie.
"I saw him."

Vic yelled, "Tattletale, tattletale.
Debbie is a tattletale."

Another day Vic climbed a tree and couldn't get down.

He yelled, "I can't get down, Debbie.
Go find Dad.
Tell him I can't get down."

Debbie didn't say a word.
She just walked into the house.

Vic sat in the tree.

He sat and sat and sat.

He sat a very long time.

At last Debbie and Dad came out
of the house.

"What took you so long?" yelled Vic.

His dad looked up and saw Vic in the
tree.

"What are you doing up there?"
asked Dad.

Vic yelled, "I can't get down.
Didn't Debbie tell you?"

"No, I didn't," said Debbie.
"I'm no tattletale!"

Tony's
Surprise

"Who has something
to tell about?"
asked Mrs. Quinn.

"I do," said Tony.
"I have a surprise
in this box."

Mrs. Quinn said, "Tell us
about it, Tony."

Tony said, "My surprise
is little and green.
It looks something like a worm now.
Soon it will make a little brown
house to live in.
It will not look like a worm when
it comes out of the house."

87

"I know what the surprise is,"
said Yoshi.
"It's a caterpillar."

"Is Yoshi right?" asked Mrs. Quinn.
"Do you have a caterpillar, Tony?"

"Yes, I do," said Tony.
"And now I'll show it to you."

Tony opened the box.

He looked and looked.

But he could not find the caterpillar.

All he could find was a brown bump

on one of the leaves.

Tony laughed.

"I thought I was going to surprise

you with my caterpillar," he said.

"But the caterpillar has surprised me.

He has made his little brown house.

He's in a cocoon."

Circle of Life

The caterpillar comes out of the egg.

The moth lays an egg.

The caterpillar makes a cocoon.

The moth comes out of the cocoon.

The Tickle Rhyme

by Ian Serraillier

"Who's that tickling my back?" said the wall.

"Me," said a small

Caterpillar. "I'm learning

To crawl."

"The Tickle Rhyme" from *The Tale of the Monster Horse* by Ian Serraillier, published by Oxford University Press and reprinted with their permission.

Cocoon

by David McCord

The little caterpillar creeps

Awhile before in silk it sleeps.

It sleeps awhile before it flies,

And flies awhile before it dies,

And that's the end of three good tries.

How to Get

an Ice Cream Cone

One day Sandy found a penny.

It was a shiny, new penny.

Sandy wanted an ice cream cone.

But she could not get one for a penny.

Sandy met Cedric.

Cedric had a magnet.

"I'll trade you," said Sandy.

"I'll trade you a penny for the magnet."

Cedric wanted some bubble gum.

He could get bubble gum for a penny.

So Cedric said, "All right.

I'll trade you."

Soon Sandy met Max.

Max had a butterfly in a jar.

"I'll trade you," said Sandy.

"I'll trade my magnet for your butterfly."

Max wanted a magnet.

He had wanted one for a long time.

So Max said, "All right.

I'll trade you."

Sandy met Amy Lee.

Amy Lee said, "Look at this button.
I found it."

Sandy said, "I'll trade you.
I'll trade my butterfly for the button."

Amy Lee wanted the butterfly.
She had wanted one for a long time.
So Amy Lee said, "All right.
I'll trade you."

Sandy saw Mrs. Bradford.

Sandy said, "Look, Mrs. Bradford.
I have a shiny button."

"That's my button!" said Mrs. Bradford.
"I lost it.
You can see where it came off my coat."

"Yes, I can," said Sandy.

And she gave the button to Mrs. Bradford.

"Thank you Sandy," said Mrs. Bradford.

Mrs. Bradford was very happy to get her button back.

So she got an ice cream cone for Sandy.

Sandy sat on the front steps to eat the cone.

She said to herself, "This is my lucky day.

I found a penny.

I traded the penny for a magnet.

I traded the magnet for a butterfly.

I traded the butterfly for a button.

I gave the button to Mrs. Bradford.

And she got me an ice cream cone.

I guess I got an ice cream cone for a penny after all."

This Man Went Away

by John Ciardi

I met a man that was all mine.

He was round and thin and all a-shine.

He had no feet, but he came to me.

He had one eye, but he couldn't see.

He had no fingers, he had no thumb,

But still he gave me a stick of gum.

And then he was gone. He was mine no more,

And I went home alone from the store.

If you want to know who he is, ask Jenny:

She gave him to me.

—Yes, A BRAND NEW PENNY!

100

Albert and the Big Balloon

One day Albert got a balloon.

Albert's friends said, "Come on, Albert.

Blow up your balloon.

Let's see how big you can blow it."

So Albert began to blow.
The balloon got bigger and
bigger and bigger.

Soon the balloon began to go
up, and Albert went with it.

Albert's friends yelled, "Let go!
Let go, Albert!   Let go!"
But Albert was afraid to let go.

Albert started yelling, "Help, help!"

But there was no one to hear him.

He was way, way up now.

BUMP!   Albert landed on something.

BUMP!   Something landed right next

to Albert.

It was a rocket.

A man got out of the rocket.

The man jumped up and down.

He yelled, "I made it!

I got to the moon all by myself."

Then the man saw Albert.

"How did you get here?" he asked.

"My balloon took off," said Albert.

"I was afraid to let go.

So I came with it.

Will you take me home in your rocket?"

"I'll take you home," said the man.
"But first I have some work to do.
You can help me."

Albert and the man put a flag
at the very top of a moon hill.
Then Albert helped the man pick up
some moon rocks.
They put the moon rocks in a box.

Albert put the box into the rocket.
Then he and the man got in.

Three, two, one, LIFT OFF!
Away went the rocket.

Albert looked back at the moon.
"Seeing the moon was fun," said
Albert.
"But going home is better."

John's Balloon

by Anne Commons

John had a balloon
That went to the moon.
He told me so.

Outside in the park,
Before it got dark,
He let it go.

It went up so high,
    A dot in the sky —
John could still see.

And then his balloon
    Bumped into the moon,
So John told me.

The moon has a spot,
    A little black dot —
What else could it be?

Acknowledgments

Book cover and title page designed by Bradford/Cout Graphic Design.

The illustrations in this book are by:

Rod Ruth (pp. 5, 90-92), Ted Carr (pp. 6, 32), Peter Dugan (pp. 7-17), Jack White (pp. 18-19, 76-78, 85-89), Dick Scott (pp. 20-21), Tony Paul (pp. 22, 110-111), Tye Gibson (pp. 23-29), Krystyna Stasiak-Orska (pp. 30-31), Phoebe Moore (pp. 33-40), Star Bellei (pp. 41-52), Carl Carter, Jr. (pp. 53-58), Richard E. Loehle (pp. 63-71), Matthew Delfino, Jr. (pp. 79-84), Lois Axeman (pp. 93-99), Justin Wager (pp. 101-109).

The photographs in this book are courtesy of:

Walter Chandoha (pp. 59-62), United Press International (p. 73), *The Chicago Tribune* (p. 74), NASA (p. 75).

"Rain" from *A Child's Garden of Verses* by Robert Louis Stevenson.

7 8 9 10 11 12 13 14 15 16 17 18 19 20   A   75 74 73 72 71